CONTE

JUDY MANN [née Gruneberg] has been a teacher at Michael Sobell Sinai School in London since 1985. During that time, she has been narrating Pete Stories to enthusiastic children. She lives in London with her husband David and son Daniel.

In 1997, she wrote a book including some of her Pete stories, which was very successful and widely acclaimed. The adventures of the lively siblings, Pete and Rifka, have amused many young children. After numerous requests from fellow teachers, parents and pupils, she has again put pen to paper and has written this new book.

www.petestories.com

MARTYN NIMAN is the creative director of 'King Bee Animation', a successful animation studio specialising in TV and Web Animation: www.kingbee.co.uk
Martyn also runs a web and graphic design agency 'Graphic Appeal' : www.graphicappeal.com.

When he's not animating and designing, Martyn enjoys time with his wife Gabby and two sons Samuel and Rafi who have been a huge inspiration for all of the illustrations in Pete Stories 2.

THE BIRTHDAY PARTY

Once upon a time, there was a little boy called Pete, who had a sister called Rifka and a best friend called Simon.

One morning, Pete was in the kitchen eating his breakfast. He shouted, "it's my birthday tomorrow and I am having a party after school. I can't wait to get lots of presents!"

He was going to be six years old. How old are you?

Mum had bought him a present the previous day and she put it in her bedroom drawer. But who do you think saw her put it there? Rifka.

Rifka was very jealous because she wanted a birthday present too, even though it wasn't her birthday! When Mum left the bedroom, Rifka ran in, took the present, and hid it under her bed. What a naughty girl she was!

The next morning, Pete woke up, jumped out of bed and screamed, "yippee it's my birthday today!" He woke up Rifka and ran into his Mum and Dad's bedroom. They sang Happy Birthday to him in their loudest voices.

Mum said, "close your eyes Pete, and I will give you your present." She went to the drawer to get his present, but she couldn't find it.

Where was it? Mum was certain that she had put it in the drawer. She could not understand why it had disappeared. We know what has happened to the present, don't we?

Pete was very disappointed but he hoped that his Mum would find it later that day. What a good and sensible boy he was. Would you behave like that? I wonder...

The children got washed, dressed and davened.
After that they went into the kitchen and there on the kitchen table was a beautiful birthday cake. It was in the shape of a number 6, covered in chocolate icing.

"Wow, what a cool cake, thanks Mum," said Pete.
The cake was for the birthday party after school.
Rifka kept very quiet about the missing present.

Suddenly the phone rang, it was Grandma Betty singing 'Happy Birthday' in her loudest voice. Pete had to hold the phone a long way from his ear! He told Grandma about the missing present.

At that moment Rifka's face turned very red, but no one noticed. But we know why, don't we?
Pete went to school with a happy smile and Mum took Rifka to nursery.

When Mum came home, she decided to clean the house. First she went upstairs to clean the children's bedrooms. What a mess Pete's bedroom was in. Toys, clothes and even his books were lying all over the floor. As it was Pete's birthday, she decided to clear it all up. What a good Mum she was.

Then she went to Rifka's room, which was very tidy. But do you know what's going to happen next?

While Mum was hoovering under the bed, the hoover kept hitting against something hard. What do you think it was? Mum got down on her hands and knees to look under the bed, and guess what she found?

Yes, you are right, it was Pete's birthday present.
Mum could not believe it! What a naughty girl Rifka was.

After cleaning the house it was time to collect Rifka from nursery. Rifka came out skipping from the classroom with a big smile on her face, so happy to see her Mum.

"What did you do today Rifka?" asked Mum.
"We made biscuits and played," Rifka answered.
"What did you do today, Mum?" asked Rifka.
"Well, I cleaned the bedrooms this morning. What do you think I found when I cleaned YOUR bedroom?"

Rifka's face went bright red and she started to cry, "it's not fair, I wanted a birthday present too."

Rifka stopped crying and whispered, "please don't tell Pete.
I won't do it again - really I won't."
"OK it's our secret," promised Mum.

Rifka gave Mum a big hug. Then they both went home to get
the birthday tea ready. Mum explained, "you did a very
naughty thing, you mustn't be so jealous, how would you like
it if Pete took your birthday present?"

It was half past three in the afternoon and Mum took Pete home from school. He was so excited that his friends were coming for tea.

"Mum," Pete asked, "have you found my present yet?"
Mum said, "yes, it is on the kitchen table."
Pete asked, "where did you find it?"
Mum replied, " ah, that is a secret!"

At that moment, Pete was not interested in the secret, all he wanted was his present. There on the kitchen table was a square box covered in bright blue shiny paper. Pete ripped off the paper, and there it was, the toy that he had been hoping for, a remote control car.

Suddenly there was a knock on the door. His friends had arrived with lovely presents and birthday cards for him.
Mum shouted, "come in, let's start the party and have fun!"

Pete had a fantastic party. They played pass the parcel, putting the tail on the donkey, dead lions and lots of other games. Mum made them fish fingers and chips for tea.

Grandma Betty who also came to the party turned off the lights in the room.
Mum brought in the birthday cake. There were six candles shining brightly.

Everyone sang and shouted, "hip hooray!" Then Pete took a deep breath and blew out all the candles in one go.

What a lovely time the children had.
Then it was time for Pete's friends to go home.

"Bye Pete, and thank you," they all said politely.
After that Pete opened his presents and let Rifka help him.
He had received lots of exciting toys and games.

Pete was still curious, "I had a great day, but Mum tell me, what REALLY happened to my missing present?"
Mum replied, "you don't need to know."

She smiled at Rifka and winked, "that's our secret!"

SUCCOT

Pete and Rifka were so excited that Succot was coming. They always enjoyed building the Succah and putting up their lovely decorations.

The Sunday before Succot, Dad built a Succah out of wood. It took him a long time to build and he was very pleased at how it looked. There was room for eight people to sit in the Succah.

Do you remember how many days Succot lasts for?

Mum had helped Dad hang up the children's decorations from school.

This year, Pete had made a hanging mobile of pretend fruit. It was covered in lots of different colour glitter. Rifka had drawn a picture of a Succah. She put leaves on her picture for the roof. She drew her family sitting around the table. Rifka was very proud of it.

Now the decorations were up and the Succah was ready for them to use.

13

The children helped Mum lay the table for Yomtov, it looked beautiful.
All that was needed now was good weather, and lots of visitors to come. However, no one had heard the bad weather report that morning. Guess what, the forecast was wind and rain - oh no!

Grandma Betty and Uncle Joe were coming for supper. Mum made chicken soup, roast chicken, tzimmus, roast potatoes and for dessert there was chocolate mousse. Yum yum!

When Yomtov arrived, Pete went to Shul with the men, and the women lit the candles.

Pete saw his best friend Simon in Shul and they were telling each other how many decorations they had in their Succah. Pete's Dad told them to be quiet. "SH SH BE QUIET!"

After Shul Pete wished Simon Chag Sameach.

While they were walking home from Shul, Pete told his Dad that he couldn't wait to be in the Succah and to show his decorations to the family.

The men arrived home and shouted out, "Chag Sameach, let's go in the Succah now and make Kiddush."

Uncle Joe walked into the Succah with Grandma Betty.
"Wow this looks wonderful, who made these decorations?"
"We did!" shouted the children jumping up and down in excitement.

Everyone was standing around the table waiting for Dad to pour the wine into his Kiddush cup.

All of a sudden, there was a pitter-patter noise on the s'chach that was on the Succah roof.

"Oh no!" shouted Pete, as a big drop of water landed on his nose.
"Go away rain, come back another day!" screamed Rifka.

Dad said, "I will make Kiddush now before the weather gets any worse."
Suddenly, a strong gust of wind started to shake the Succah. Before Dad had even finished making Kiddush, the wind made the Succah tremble even more. The Succah was like a lulav, shaking left, right, up and down! Oh no!

The Succah began to creak from side to side. Uncle Joe said nervously, "do you see what I am seeing? The Succah is moving!"
"Oh no, it is going to fall down!" screamed Mum.

At that moment, the wind howled and whistled, the rain poured and poured. You know what's going to happen next, don't you?

The Succah wobbled, crashed to the floor and broke into pieces. There was nothing left of the beautiful Succah that Dad had built.

The decorations flew around in the wind and the family watched as the decorations flew up into the sky. All their hard work had flown away.

Pete and Rifka just burst into tears. No one could believe their eyes - it was like a bad dream.

Uncle Joe looked around and saw everyone's sad faces. "Come on, let's go back inside the house and eat Mum's tasty meal." The children dried their eyes and Mum gave them each a hug.

Mum asked them, "does this remind you of the story of the three little pigs and the big bad wolf?"
Rifka replied, "I know that story, when the wolf blew the pigs' huts down, except there is no wolf here!"

Dad had to make Kiddush again. Then the family went into the kitchen to wash their hands for hamotzie.
Dad made the bracha for the challot and everyone sat down and ate the challah quietly.
Pete and Rifka just looked so sad.
"Don't worry, I'll think of something," suggested Dad.

Suddenly, there was a knock at the door. Who could it be? Dad opened the door. It was Simon and his family. They had a Succah inside their house with an opening roof, so their Succah was fine in this terrible weather.

When Simon saw the bad weather he thought straight away, poor Pete, his Succah must have fallen down. He said to his parents, "lets invite them to eat in our Succah."

What a kind family they were. Pete's family were so pleased that they had somewhere to eat for Succot.
The following day Pete's family went to eat at Simon's house and they all had a good time.

For the rest of Succot, their friends invited the family out.

Dad said that next year, he would have to build an even stronger Succah, with more nails and screws so that not even the wind or rain would blow it away.

That was a Chag that the family will never forget.

DOING A MITZVAH.

This story is about Pete and Rifka doing a mitzvah. Do you know what a mitzvah is? It means doing a good deed.

One Sunday morning, Mum had a bad headache and a cold. She couldn't get out of bed because she felt so poorly. Dad was in Shul davening.
"Mum, we'll do something special to make you feel better." Pete said kindly.

Pete and Rifka tiptoed downstairs and went to the kitchen. Pete said to Rifka, "I will make Mum some breakfast and you can help me. Go into the cupboard and take out a bowl." Rifka was very good and did as she was told.

As she was taking the bowl over to Pete, she tripped over and it smashed onto the floor. "Aaaah, oh no!" they shouted but they didn't even bother to clear it up.

Pete then got a new bowl out of the cupboard.

Pete went into the larder and took out a box of cornflakes and poured some into the bowl. But, guess what...too much came out and it landed all over the table and onto the floor! Rifka started to laugh, as she was walked around the kitchen, she heard the sound of crunch, crunch under her feet.

Pete shouted "STOP THAT!" But they still didn't clear up the mess.

Pete went to the fridge...What do you think he went to get? Yes, that's right.... milk. But what do you think happened next?

Yes - he poured far too much milk and it spilt right over the edge of the bowl onto the table and then onto the kitchen floor.
Rifka started giggling again, "if we pour sugar on top, it will look like a mountain!"

At that moment, they heard the key turning in the front door. Guess who was coming home from shul?

The kitchen door creaked open. Dad popped his head round the door and saw Rifka and Pete giggling.

His eyes nearly popped out of his head! He couldn't believe the terrible mess, what would Mum say?

Pete and Rifka jumped when they saw Dad at the door. They shouted, " Dad, Dad, Mum is not well and we tried to make her breakfast but it was much too hard for us."

Dad joked, "are you sure you are not making it for the animals in the zoo, with THIS mess on the floor?"

Rifka started to cry, "please don't tell Mum, we were only trying to help."
Dad gave a deep sigh, got hold of the dustpan and brush and started to clear up.

He gave Rifka a hug, " I know you both tried to do a mitzvah to make Mum some breakfast because she is ill. But let me show you how to make a proper breakfast."

Dad then showed the children how to make breakfast properly. Rifka drew a picture of a pretty flower and put it on the tray next to Mum's cornflakes.

Dad carried the tray upstairs with the children following behind him.

Mum was so happy and whispered, "I'm so proud of you both that you made this lovely breakfast for me."
Dad winked at the children and said, "so am I!"

By late afternoon Mum was feeling so much better that she came down for supper.
She phoned Grandma Betty to say how proud she was of the children for making her breakfast.

But the family never told her what had really happened with the breakfast.

Do you think that she will ever know?

CHANUKAH

Pete and Rifka were very excited that Chanukah was coming. They loved lighting the Menorah, eating latkes and playing with the dreidal.

What do you like doing on Chanukah?

In school, Pete was going to make his Menorah out of clay. He was going to use it at home.

Their teacher, Mrs Cohen discussed with them how they would decorate the Menorah. They could use paints and glitter.

Mrs Cohen told the children that they needed to make nine holes, eight for the candles and one for the Shamash.

Pete and his best friend Simon had such fun making and decorating the Menorah.

In fact they did not even have an argument about it. They just got on with it quietly, which as you know is unusual for those boys.

Mrs Cohen was very pleased with their work and told the children that their Menorahs would be ready to take home for Chanukah.

Pete was very excited about his Menorah and told his Mum how hard he had worked on it.

A week later at home time, Pete ran into the playground, and shouted to his Mum, "look what I made."

Mum looked at the Menorah. "What a beautiful Menorah, look after it carefully until we get home, and then I will put it in a safe place for you."

Pete went into his mum's car holding the Menorah very carefully. Mum drove home very slowly so that the Menorah would not break.

When Pete arrived home, in his excitement he ran into the house but he did not look where he was going. Suddenly Pete tripped over Rifka's toys and he fell flat on his face.

"Oh no!" he cried.

"What is the matter, Pete?" shouted Mum.
"My Menorah has fallen on the floor and now it is broken into tiny pieces. I can't light my Menorah and I can't do the mitzvah."
Poor Pete could not stop crying.

Mum took one look at the Menorah and saw that it was in small pieces. There was no way it could be repaired. She gave Pete a big hug.

However, Mum had a big surprise for him. Do you know what it was?

"Pete, stop crying and I will see what I can do, " she said. Mum went upstairs to look in her special cupboard. She took a parcel out and came downstairs. Do you know what it was in the parcel?
Mum said. "Pete, come here, I have something special for you."

Pete could not wait to open the parcel and ripped it open. He could not believe his eyes.

There it was, a beautiful shining Menorah that Mum and Dad had bought for him many months ago. It was silver with each candleholder a different colour.

"Wow, Mum this is a fabulous Menorah. Thank you, now I can do the mitzvah."

That night, when Pete lit the Menorah, he was the happiest boy ever. The candles shone brightly on the window sill. Pete had a wonderful Chanukah.

I hope that you do too.

PETE IN THE SNOW

One cold morning, Pete looked out of his window and couldn't believe his eyes. It looked like 'Snow Wonderland'.

The grass and the roofs of the houses were covered with lots of snow. It looked so beautiful.

"Yippee," Pete shouted, waking up Mum, Dad and Rifka. Everyone was so excited. The children kept on jumping on their bed and around the room shouting, "it's snowing, it's snowing."

All of a sudden, the telephone began to ring. It was Pete's teacher to say that there was no school today because of the snow. Pete shouted, "hooray, hooray, no school today, in the snow we can play, hip hip hooray!"

"Mum, can we go out and play in the snow now?" asked Pete. Mum answered, "no, first wash your face and hands, brush your teeth and daven.

After they had porridge for breakfast, Rifka and Pete ran out into the snow, wearing their hats, coats, scarves and warm boots. Rifka had never seen so much snow before. Her eyes were bright with amazement.

"Come on Rifka, let's build a big snowman," shouted Pete. The children made a snowball and then rolled it in the snow around the garden. It became bigger and bigger until they could not roll anymore as it was too big. This was the body of the snowman. Then the children rolled out a smaller ball of snow for its head.

Pete and Rifka put a carrot on its face for its nose, two pieces of potatoes for his eyes and lots of raisins for its happy smile. They danced around the snowman singing, "hip hooray, we built a snowman today, it looks like Uncle Ray!!!"

Then Mum called Pete and Rifka to come into the house for some hot chocolate. The children were ready for the hot drink as they were very cold. Brrrrrrrrrrrrrr!

They took off their wet clothes and put on some dry ones. They took a blanket and snuggled up near the radiator with their hot drink.

Then Pete and Rifka played with their toys inside the house. After that, they had supper and went to bed early, as they were so tired from running around in the snow.

The following morning, it was still snowing, and there was no school again.
Pete asked Mum, "can Simon come round and play today?"

Mum agreed and phoned Simon's Mum to arrange a time for Simon to come round.

Pete and Rifka washed, dressed and davened. Then they had a lovely breakfast.

All of a sudden the doorbell rang. Guess, who it was? - Simon.

The boys were happy to see each other and they ran into the garden. It was snowing very heavily and it was so cold. Brrrrrrrrr.

"Look at the snowman that we made yesterday." Pete said proudly.

Simon looked at the snowman standing in the garden but did not say anything. He was jealous because the one that he had made in his garden did not look as good as Pete's.

So Simon decided to do something very naughty. Do you know what he was going to do?

While Pete was not looking, Simon went up to the snowman and pushed its head off and it crashed to the ground.
What a very naughty thing to do!
"Oh dear, look what has happened to the head!" said Simon sarcastically.
Pete could not believe his eyes, there on the ground, was the remains of the snowman's head.
"What happened?" asked Pete.
"I don't know, answered Simon. Do you think that he is telling the truth?

Simon had a big smirk on his face. Luckily for Pete, someone was watching from the upstairs bedroom and saw what Simon had done.
It was Rifka, and she burst into tears.
Mum heard her and rushed into the room.
"What is the matter?" she asked.

Rifka told Mum what she had seen in the garden.
Mum could not believe her ears. They both ran downstairs and went into the kitchen to look out of the window.
Then Mum and Rifka saw Simon knocking down the body of the snowman.

Pete saw what Simon had done, and the boys started to have a fight.

BAM WAM BASH!!!

Mum ran out and screamed at the top of her voice, "STOP!" Both of the boys looked up and Mum pulled them apart.

"Simon - why did you knock down the snowman?" she asked. He started to cry. "Because your snowman is better than mine. Its not fair!"

Mum calmed down the boys and said to Simon, "just because you think our snowman is better, you can't just knock our snowman down."

Instead of being angry and sending Simon home, Mum said, "say sorry to Pete, and let's make an even bigger snowman." Simon did as he was told and the boys shook hands with each other. They were friends again.

Everyone had such a wonderful time making another snowman. It was even bigger than Mum!
Simon, Pete and Rifka had such a giggle making its face - it looked like the boys' headmaster Mr Levy!

They put a hat on its head and gave it a smile that was made out of small stones. Then they put oranges for its eyes. It looked great.
After that they went back into the house to have hot chocolate. Mmmmmmmmmm.

Then it was time for Simon to go home. His Mum came to collect him and no one said anything about what had happened that morning.

For many days afterwards, the snowman stood in the garden. What a great snowman it looked.

Dad took a picture of the snowman with his camera, with Pete and Rifka standing proudly besides it.

PURIM

It was Purim, one of the most exciting festivals of the Jewish year. Pete and Simon were dressing up and were going to wear their costumes at the school Purim parade.

They were dressing up as their favourite comic characters.

Pete and Simon went to school together brimming with excitement.
They had gifts of Mishloach Manot to give to their teacher Mrs Cohen.

At school there was going to be a Megillah reading, a fancy dress parade and hamantashen for lunch. "I can't wait to eat the hamantashen. I am going to eat thousands of them." Simon boasted.
Pete said, "don't be so silly."

Off they went into the classroom and sang. "Happy Purim" to Mrs Cohen and gave her Mishloach Manot. She put them on her table and said. "Thank you so much boys."
Pete and Simon could not believe the amount of delicious food that was piled on the table.

After Mrs Cohen had taken the register the children davened. Then it was time to go into the hall to show off their costumes and hear the Megillah. All the children were so excited. The only way the head teacher, Mr Levy, could get the children to be quiet was to have two big signs. One had 'Stop' written on it and the other had 'Noise' written on it.

Mr Levy said to the children, "every time you hear the wicked man Haman mentioned when we read the Megillah, I will put the sign up that says 'Noise', but when I want quiet then the other sign will go up."

That worked very well. When the children heard Haman's name, they made so much noise that the poor teachers had to put their fingers in their ears!

After the Megillah reading, the children were ready to go into the playground. However the teachers were ready to have a strong cup of tea!

Pete and Simon had a different idea. They looked at each other and whispered, "let's go into the classroom and eat some of Mrs Cohen's Mishloach Manot."
Was that a good thing to do? No, that was a VERY naughty thing to do.

You wouldn't do that, would you???

They tiptoed into the classroom, looking left and right to make sure that no one had seen them. They hid under the table and started to eat the Mishloach Manot. Their hands reached out and up to grab the tasty food.

They ate all the sweets, chocolate, hamantashen and crisps Yum Yum!

As you can imagine, Pete and Simon started to feel very sick and started to make funny noises. ARGH ARGH ARGH!! At that moment the bell went for the end of break, and the other children came back into the classroom.

Mrs Cohen walked into the classroom and gasped! She could not believe her eyes. There in front of her, were crumbs, wrappers and four little legs sticking out from under the table. "WHAT IS GOING ON HERE??? WHOEVER IS UNDER THE TABLE, COME OUT NOW!"

Pete and Simon came out from under the table, looking green and feeling very sick. "What have you two been doing?" shouted Mrs Cohen, angrily.

The two boys' lips began to quiver and they whispered, "we are very sorry Mrs Cohen."
Mrs Cohen was furious and told them that they had been very naughty to take food without permission.

The boys looked so sad and ill.

Simon said, "we are very sorry that we ate your food, but we thought that we would help you out. It would have been too much for YOU to eat all that on your own!!"
Mrs Cohen looked at their pale faces and she could not tell them off.

In fact, the boys felt so sick that the school nurse had to phone the boys' Mums to take them home. Their parents were not very happy with them and made them write a letter of apology to Mrs Cohen.

But, do you know what the worst thing about being sent home was, they missed a most wonderful Purim at school. They missed the Purim parade, clowns coming to entertain the children and hamentashen to eat.

The boys learnt their lesson, and they never did it again!

PETE AND THE DOCTOR

One sunny morning Pete woke up with a sore throat. His Mum came into his bedroom to wake him up, as it was time for breakfast.
She saw that he looked really miserable lying in bed. "What's the matter darling?" she asked.
"My throat is very sore," he croaked. Mum checked his forehead and it felt very hot.

She went downstairs to telephone the doctor to make an appointment. She had the first appointment of the morning, which was before Rifka had to go to her nursery.

Rifka and Pete got dressed, washed and said Modeh Ani. After breakfast they went straight to the Doctor by car.

On the way, Rifka said to Mum, "I don't feel well either, my throat hurts too."

We all know what that means. Rifka didn't want to go to nursery, she wanted to stay at home with Pete.

They got out of the car and went into the Doctor's surgery.

Doctor Murphy examined Pete. He told him to open his mouth and say Aaaaaaah.
At once, the Doctor saw that Pete's throat was very red.

Then Doctor Murphy put his stethoscope on Pete's chest and asked him to hold his breath and then breathe in and out. Doctor Murphy then put the stethoscope on Pete's back.

The stethoscope was tickling Pete, he tried to laugh but his throat hurt too much.

"Oh dear, what a red throat you have, I will have to give you some medicine to make you better," said Doctor Murphy.

"Doctor Murphy, please look at my throat, it also hurts", Rifka whimpered. Rifka then opened her mouth and Doctor Murphy grinned, "what a beautiful looking throat you have, I think you deserve a sticker."

Rifka was so excited, she couldn't wait to show all her friends at nursery, the sticker that she had received from the Doctor.

After Mum had dropped Rifka off at nursery, Mum and Pete went to the chemist to get the medicine. Mum, then took him home, gave him a spoonful of medicine and he went straight to bed.

After a couple of hours, he woke up feeling extremely hungry. Mum gave him a bowl of jelly and ice cream. Pete really enjoyed that treat.

After that, he went back to bed, and listened to stories on his CD player.

Later that afternoon, Rifka came home in a VERY bad mood. "I've got a very BAD throat too," she said in an angry voice.

Mum realised that she was jealous, and pretended to give her some medicine, which really was blackcurrant squash on a spoon!

Rifka went up to bed and pretended to be ill.
Poor Mum, she had to run up and down the stairs giving the
children drinks.

She was so exhausted that she decided to bring them down
to the lounge. Then they all fell asleep on the sofa.

When Dad came home from work, the house was very quiet and he wondered where everyone was. He called out, "hello I'm home." But he received no answer. Where was everyone? He walked into the kitchen and no one was there. Then he walked into the lounge and found them all asleep!

He couldn't believe his eyes and tiptoed around the lounge. Suddenly Mum woke up and told Dad what had happened during the day.

Dad said, "don't worry about supper, I can see that you have had a busy day. I will go and get pizza and chips from Moshe's takeaway."

Dad brought the food home. Pete was feeling so much better that he was able to eat the pizza and chips and even had seconds.
Pete said to Mum, "thanks for looking after me, I feel so much better, I want to go back to school tomorrow." Mum was really pleased.

After supper the children played with their toys. Pete took his medicine, went to bed and slept soundly.

The next morning Pete was the first one up, dressed and ready for school. When he arrived at school, all his friends ran up to him and said that they had missed him.

UNCLE JOE'S WEDDING DAY

"Hurray, Uncle Joe is getting married", shouted Pete and Rifka at the top of their voices.

Mum had told them the good news one Sunday morning. Uncle Joe was the children's favourite uncle.

Mum told them that he was going to marry a tall lady with blue eyes and black hair and her name was Dalia.

Pete and Rifka had met her once before and they liked this friendly lady. They were so excited because they had never been to a wedding before.

Mum shouted, "children calm down, I have more to tell you. The wedding will be in two months time and you are going to walk with the bride into shul."
"What does that mean?" asked Pete.
"Good question Pete. It means that when Aunty Dalia comes into Shul to marry Uncle Joe, you will walk in front of her holding a small posy of flowers."
"Yuck, not me, that's too girlish," said Pete.
Mum explained, "Of course not, Rifka will be holding the posy and you will walk next to her. She will be a bridesmaid and you will be a page boy."

Pete was happy with the arrangement and the children could not wait for the wedding to happen.

The following week, Pete, Rifka, Mum and Aunty Dalia went to the shops to choose smart outfits for the wedding. Rifka held Aunty Dalia's hand the whole time and kept smiling at her.

Aunty Dalia and Mum decided that Rifka should wear a pink dress and Pete should wear smart blue trousers, a white shirt and a gold waistcoat. The children loved their new outfits.

The day before the wedding, Mum made the children's clothes ready, and put them on the dining room table. She made sure that the children went to bed early that night.

The wedding day arrived and everyone was very excited. The children had a quiet morning as they had to get ready by two o'clock in the afternoon to have their photos taken with Aunty Dalia at her house.

Before Pete and Rifka went, Mum told them that they had to be good and not to eat any food until AFTER the wedding ceremony, as she did not want their clothes ruined.

The children listened carefully, but I think you know what is going to happen..........

The children looked very smart when they arrived at the house.

When Pete and Rifka saw the bride Aunty Dalia, they thought that she looked like a princess.

In fact Rifka said to Aunty Dalia, "you look like a princess. Can I wear your crown?" Everyone laughed.

In the room was a table full of lovely cakes and biscuits for the guests. Pete and Rifka looked at the yummy food.

The children wished that they could have some. They winked at each other and when no one was looking, Pete whispered to Rifka, "follow me, but be very quiet!"

Do you think you know what they are going to do?
Pete tiptoed to the table and quickly grabbed some delicious cream cake. He ran up to Rifka and whispered, "let's hide under the table and eat these."

The children munched their way through the cakes. The cakes were full of cream and chocolate syrup.
All of a sudden Mum shouted, " children where are you?"

Pete and Rifka looked at each other with guilty faces. At that moment, a big piece of cake fell onto Pete's white shirt. OH NO!

He tried to wipe off the cake. Instead he made it worse and the shirt was ruined. Pete looked at his shirt and became very worried.
What would his Mum say?

The children came out from under the table, looking very sheepish. Mum looked at Pete's shirt. She had a face like thunder. Oh dear, Pete is going to get into BIG trouble.

Mum took Pete into the kitchen and was extremely angry with him.
What could she do? The wedding was going to start soon.
Then she came up with a clever idea.
She phoned Simon's Mum to ask if Simon had a clean white Shabbat shirt.

Luckily he did, and Simon's mum brought round the shirt to Pete.
Pete was so relieved! He went PHEW!
He put it on and stayed with his Mum.

Mum then warned them NOT TO EAT ANYTHING until after the ceremony.

The children went in the big white wedding car with Aunty Dalia. Pete was so excited and said, " I feel like a king, I will wave to the people as we go past with my royal hand!"

When the car arrived at the shul, the children were very sensible and held each other's hand.

When it was time for the ceremony to begin, there were many guests waiting for the bride to come into shul.

Uncle Joe was already standing under the chuppah waiting for Aunty Dalia.

First, Pete and Rifka came in together and walked down the aisle. The guests thought that the children looked very cute and smart.
Then came Aunty Dalia with her parents.

Everyone gasped and thought how beautiful she looked.
The children then went to sit with their Mum in the front row of the shul.

When the ceremony began, there was a lovely choir singing and the Rabbi blessed the couple. Uncle Joe put a ring on Aunty Dalia's finger.
After that, everyone shouted Mazel Tov.

Uncle Joe and Aunty Dalia looked extremely happy.
Mum and Dad were very proud of their children.
After the chuppah, they all went to a big hall for the dinner
and to dance the night away.

The music was loud and nearly everyone was dancing. There
were speeches and lovely food. Everyone had a fantastic
time.

Pete was on his Dad's shoulders dancing. Rifka was picking
up balloons and ribbons from the floor.
In Uncle Joe's speech he thanked the children for being
such a good bridesmaid and pageboy and gave them each a
little gift.

By the time the dancing was over, Pete was still looking for some more food!!!
Rifka was asleep on Mum's lap snoring away!
zzzzzzzzzzzzzzzzzzz.

In the car on the way home Pete fell fast asleep, dreaming about the very exciting day that he had had.

PESACH

Pete was so excited, because he was going to stay up late for Seder night. He had been practising the Ma Nishtanah as well as other songs at school. He was looking forward to having four cups of grape juice, eating matza and finding the afikomen.

Pete's favourite Uncle, Joe was coming with his new wife Aunty Dalia for the Seder night.
Grandma Betty was sleeping at their house for the whole of Pesach and was helping Mum make the food.

Mum explained to Pete, "you need to have a long sleep this afternoon so that you will be wide awake this evening and be able to sing Ma-Nishtanah beautifully."

After lunch, Pete went upstairs to bed but he could not get to sleep. He was thinking about singing, eating and finding the afikomen. Tonight, Pete was going to wear his new white shirt and blue tie. He kept looking at them in the cupboard where they were hanging.

Pete kept tossing and turning but could not fall asleep. He ended up reading a comic until he finally fell asleep. But do you know what...instead of sleeping for two hours, he only slept for twenty minutes.

However his Mum didn't know this when she went to wake him up. She shook him on the shoulder, "wakey wakey, it's time to get ready for the Seder."

Pete and Rifka had a wash and got dressed into their Yomtov clothes. They looked very smart.

Suddenly, the doorbell rang and Uncle Joe and Aunty Dalia arrived. "Look at my new tie, do you like it?" Pete said proudly She answered, "you look very handsome!"

Everyone was so happy to see each other.
Rifka was very eager to start the Seder, "come on, let's start now," she said.
However, Mum explained, "its not Yomtov yet, so go and play in the meantime."

Daddy, Uncle Joe and Pete went to shul and the women lit the candles for Yomtov. The candles shone brightly in the dining room. The Seder plate on the table looked special. The Kiddush cups were very shiny, as Mum had polished them the day before.

Pete met his friend Simon at Shul and they were showing off their new ties. Pete had a blue tie and Simon had a red one. They made so much noise talking about their ties that the Rabbi stared at them as if to say, please be quiet.

The boys stopped talking, sat down quietly and davened. After the men had davened, they walked home. Pete shouted to them, " come on let's run home quickly, I can't wait for the Seder to begin!"

Finally they arrived home and everyone was excited to start the Seder. They all sat down, Dad at the top of the table and Mum at the other end. Everyone had their own Kiddush cup.

Dad began to make Kiddush, and Pete started to look very tired. Do you know why?

Soon, it was going to be Pete's turn to sing the Ma-Nishtanah. Rifka did not know it yet, as she was younger than Pete and had not learnt it.

All of a sudden, Pete's eyes started to close, his head began to droop slowly onto the table and he fell fast asleep.
Dad said, "come on Pete, it's your turn." But all that they heard was snoring! ZZZZZZZZZZZZZZZZZZZZZZZZZZ.

Everyone looked at each other and whispered, "what has happened? Why has Pete fallen asleep?" Grandma Betty said, "he probably didn't sleep long enough as he was so excited."

Everyone was disappointed. Dad carried him upstairs to bed and Uncle Joe had to say the Ma-Nishtanah. Everyone wished that it had been Pete singing as Uncle Joe's voice was not as good as Pete's!

So make sure that you all have a sleep in the afternoon before Seder night.

Rifka missed Pete at the Seder table and kept running up to his bedroom to see if he was awake, but he was still asleep. She felt very sad.

Rifka sat on Aunty Dalia's lap for the whole Seder. She only managed to knock her Kiddush cup over once. The year before she had knocked it over twice! She sang the song about the 10 plagues in such a sweet voice.

The fun part of the Seder was when Rifka and Aunty Dalia had to look for the afikomen. Do you know where Dad had hidden it? He hid it on the window sill behind the curtain. With the help of Aunty Dalia, Rifka found it.

The Seder finished very late and the family missed Pete, but they still had a lovely time.

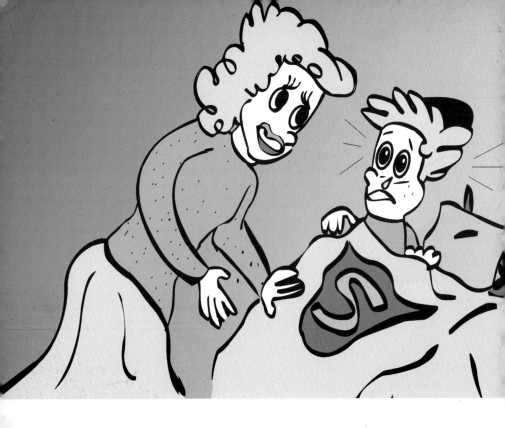

The next morning, when Pete woke up, he looked around his bedroom and tried to remember what had happened the night before.
Did he or did he not stay up for the whole Seder? He started to cry.

Mum came rushing in, "what is the matter?"
Pete sobbed and asked, "did I sing the Ma-Nishtanah last night?"
"No, you fell asleep at the table." she answered.

Pete carried on crying," NOW I will have to wait for another whole year."

Mum explained, " no, we have another Seder tonight. In Israel, the people only have one night Seder as they only keep seven days of Pesach. We have eight days of Pesach, so you are lucky that there is another Seder night. But you MUST make sure you sleep this afternoon."

"Don't worry Mum, I definitely will," Pete replied.

That afternoon, Pete had a long sleep. He slept for two hours.
After shul that evening, the family started the Seder. Pete stayed up and sang Ma-Nishtanah loudly and clearly. Everyone was so proud of him.

Who do you think found the afikomen? Yes, it was Pete, he found it in the bookcase. Everyone cheered!

They all had a lovely Seder and the only person that fell asleep at the table was Grandma Betty! I think that she had too much wine to drink!